Intro to Science

Student Diary

Intro to Science Student Diary

Updated Edition, 2018

ISBN # 978-1-935614-65-4

Printed in the USA for worldwide distribution

For more copies write to:
Elemental Science
PO Box 79
Niceville, FL 32588
support@elementalscience.com

Copyright Policy

Table of Contents

Intro to Science

Unit 1: Chemistry Diary

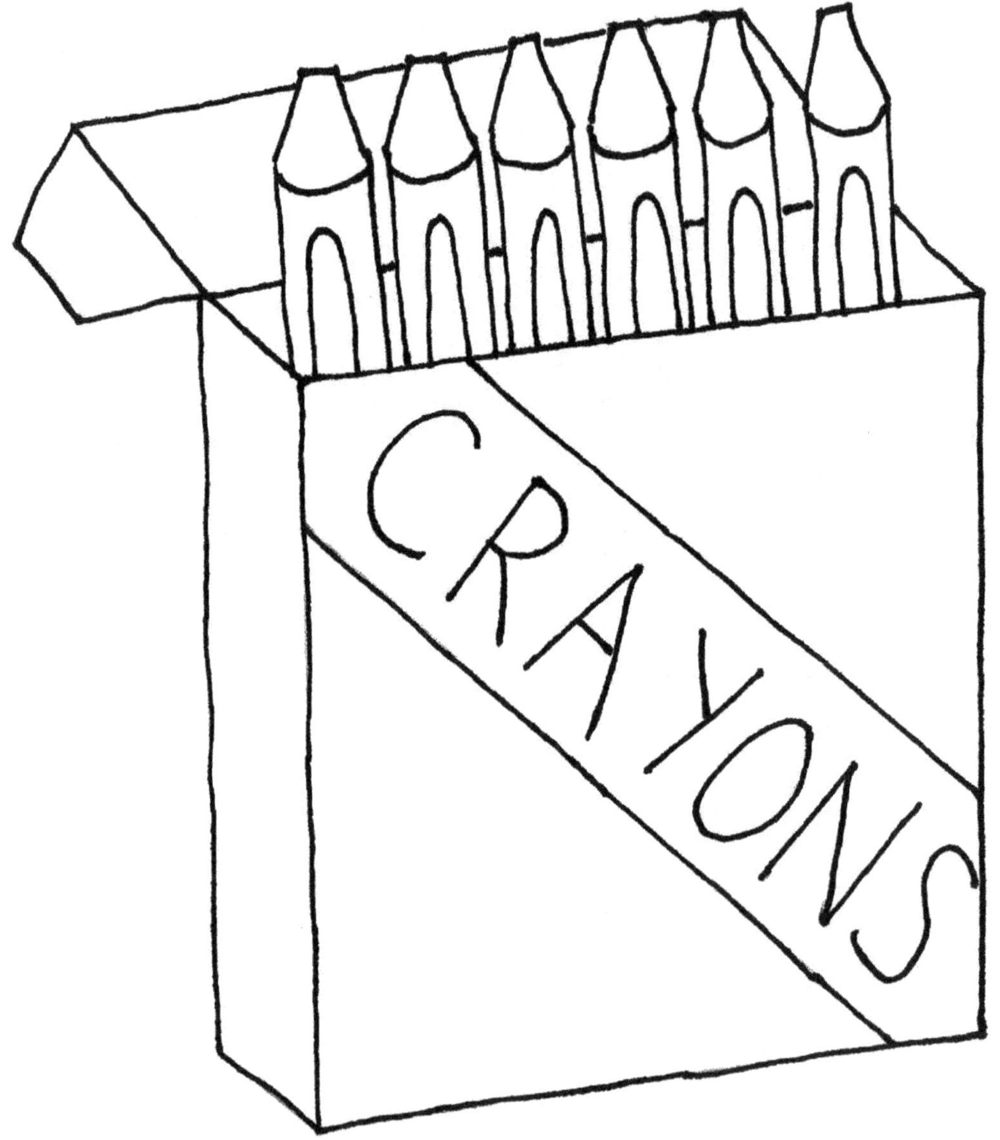

A solid melts into a liquid.

Crayon Cookies

What I learned:

Coloring with Cookies

Finding Waxy Coatings

Thick paint

Thick paint after adding water

Adding water to a solution will make it thinner or weaker.

Kool-Aid Chemistry

What I learned:

Diluted Art

Muddy Solutions

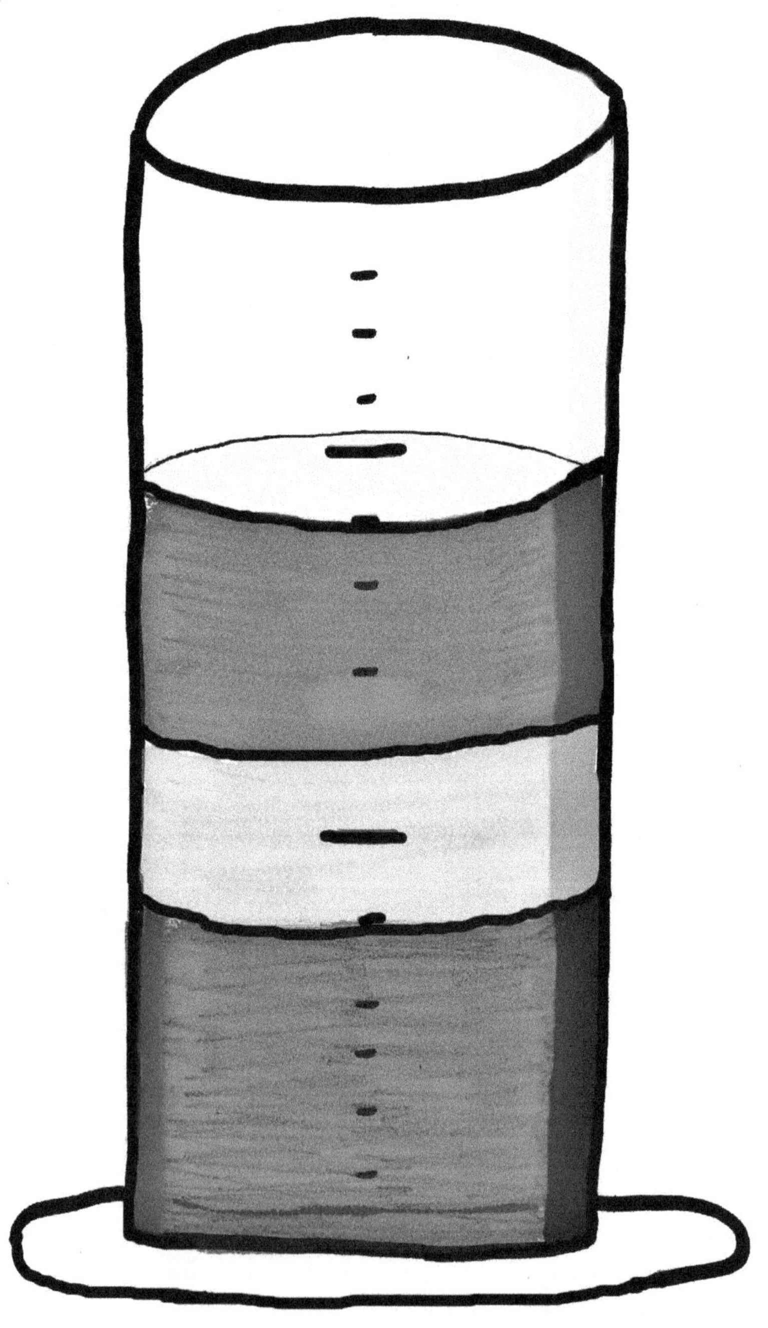

Oil is less dense than water.

How Dense is Density

Object	Sinks	Floats

Marbled Paper

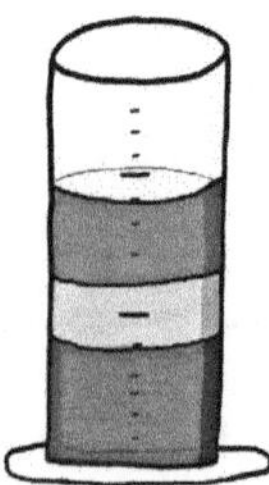

Density in Nature

Object	Sinks	Floats

What I learned:

____

____

____

____

Crystals are made up of minerals found in the earth.

How fast does your crystal grow

What I learned:

Sparkling Rock

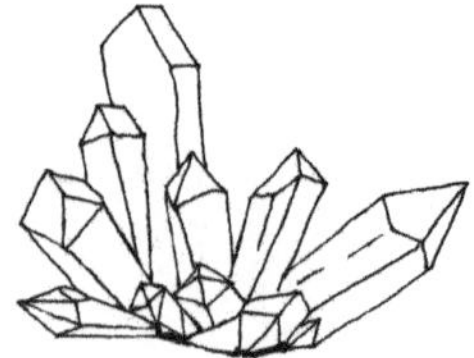

Quartz

Our two colors

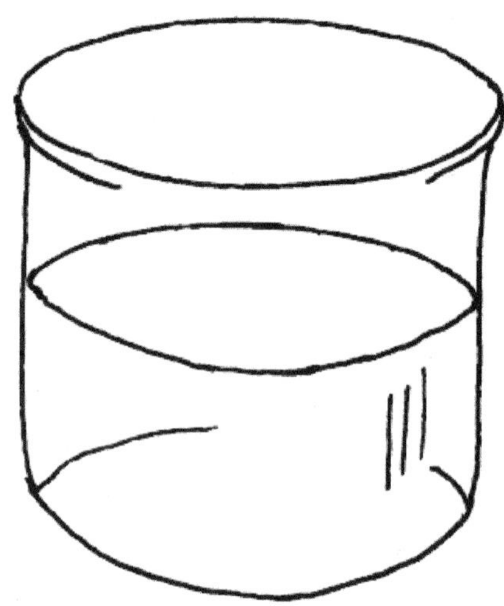

What happened when we mixed the colors

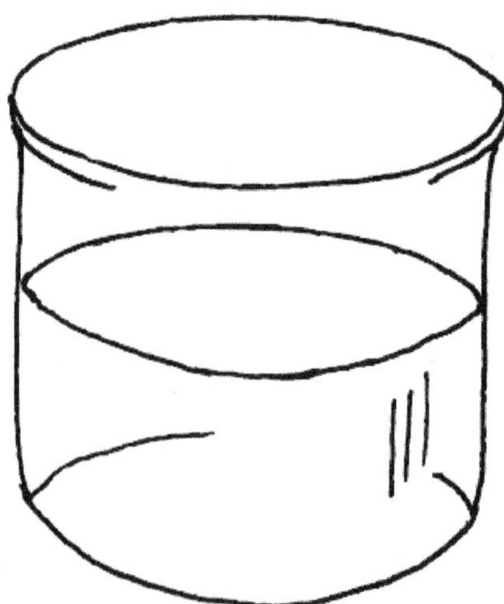

Two colors can be mixed to make a new color.

Colored Water Chemistry

What I learned:

Color Painting

Colors in Nature

When water freezes,
it changes into ice.

Brrr–It's Cold

Liquid	Did it freeze?
	Yes No
	Yes No
	Yes No
	Yes No
	Yes No

What I learned:

____

____

____

____

Ice Painting

Weather Observation

Intro to Science

Unit 2: Physics Diary

Gravity is the force that pulls all things to the ground.

Galileo's Drop

What I learned:

Gravity Drops

Apple Tree

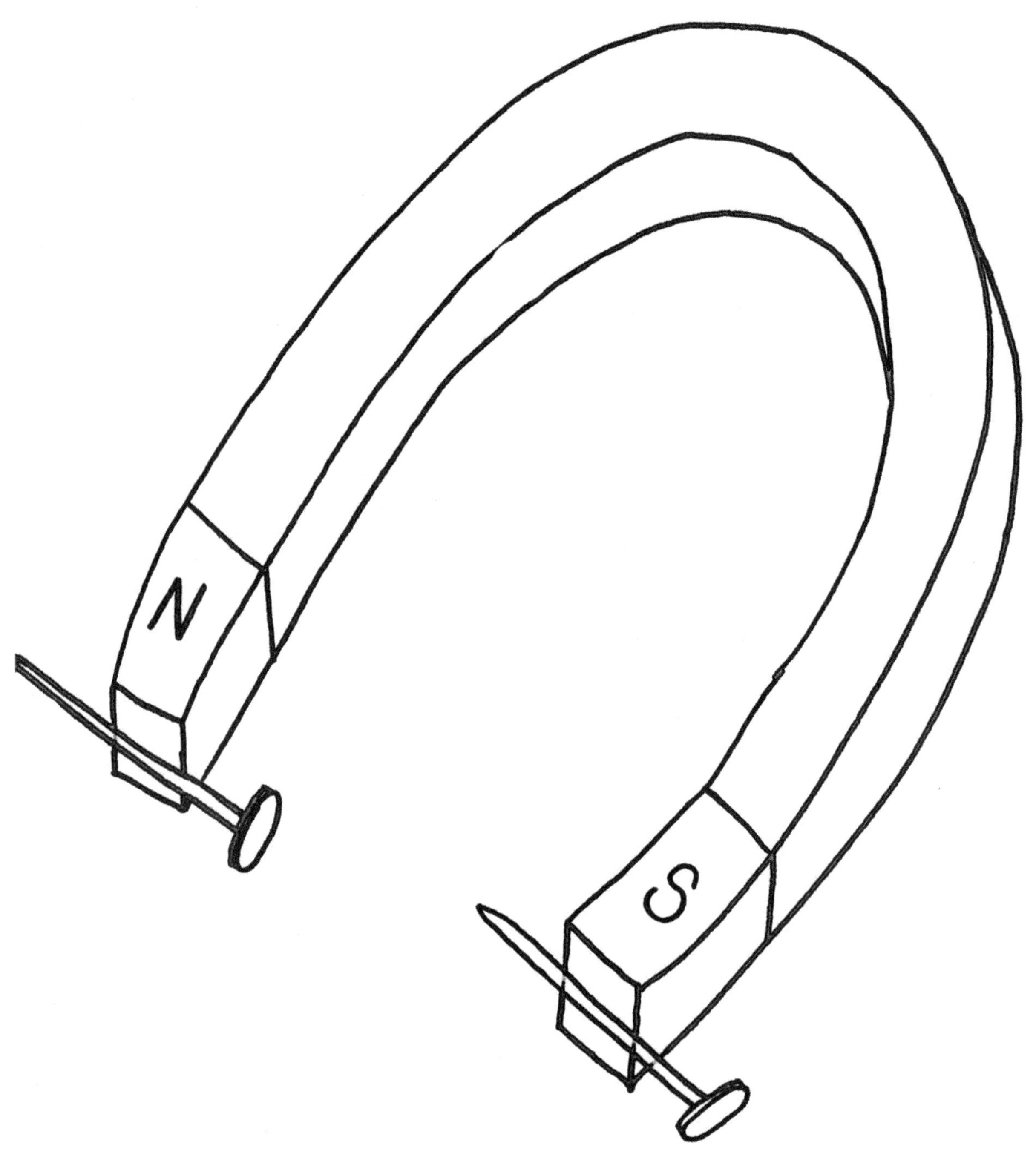

Magnets are attracted
to certain kinds of metal.

Are you attracted to me?

Object	Was it attracted to the magnet?
	Yes No
	Yes No
	Yes No
	Yes No
	Yes No
	Yes No
	Yes No

Painting with Magnets

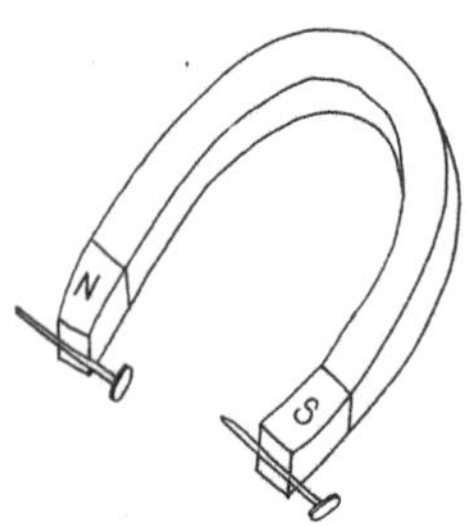

Magnetism in Nature

Object	Was it attracted to the magnet?
	Yes No
	Yes No
	Yes No
	Yes No
	Yes No

What I learned:

____

____

____

____

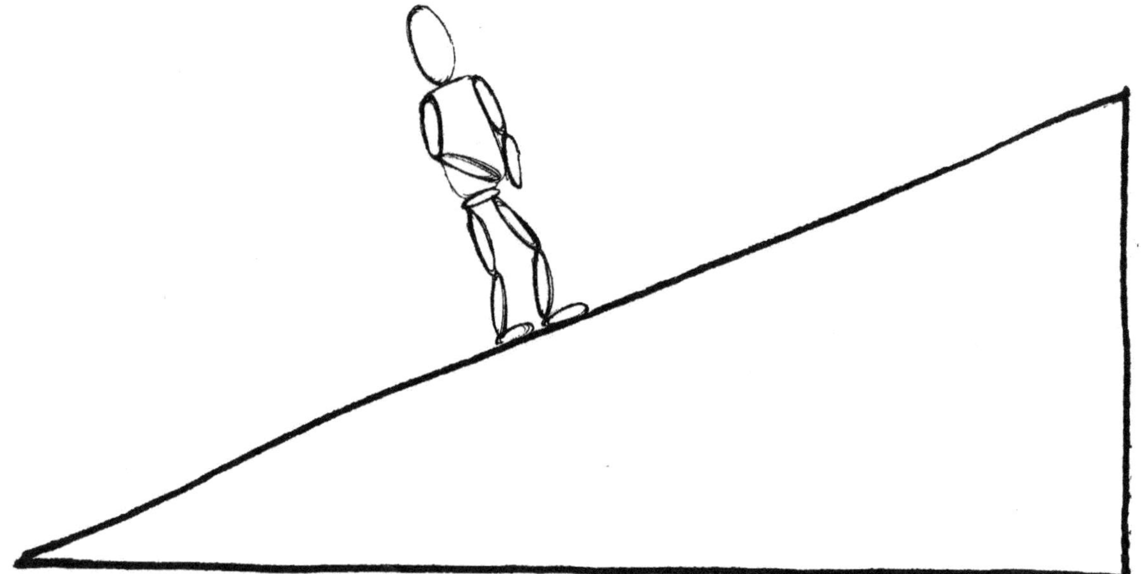

A ramp is called an inclined plane.

Rolling Along

What I learned:

Ramp Painting

Ramps in Nature

Static electricity is
an electrical charge that attracts.

Static Electricity Tester

Object	Was it attracted?
	Yes No
	Yes No
	Yes No
	Yes No
	Yes No
	Yes No
	Yes No

Dancing Electrons

Weather Observation

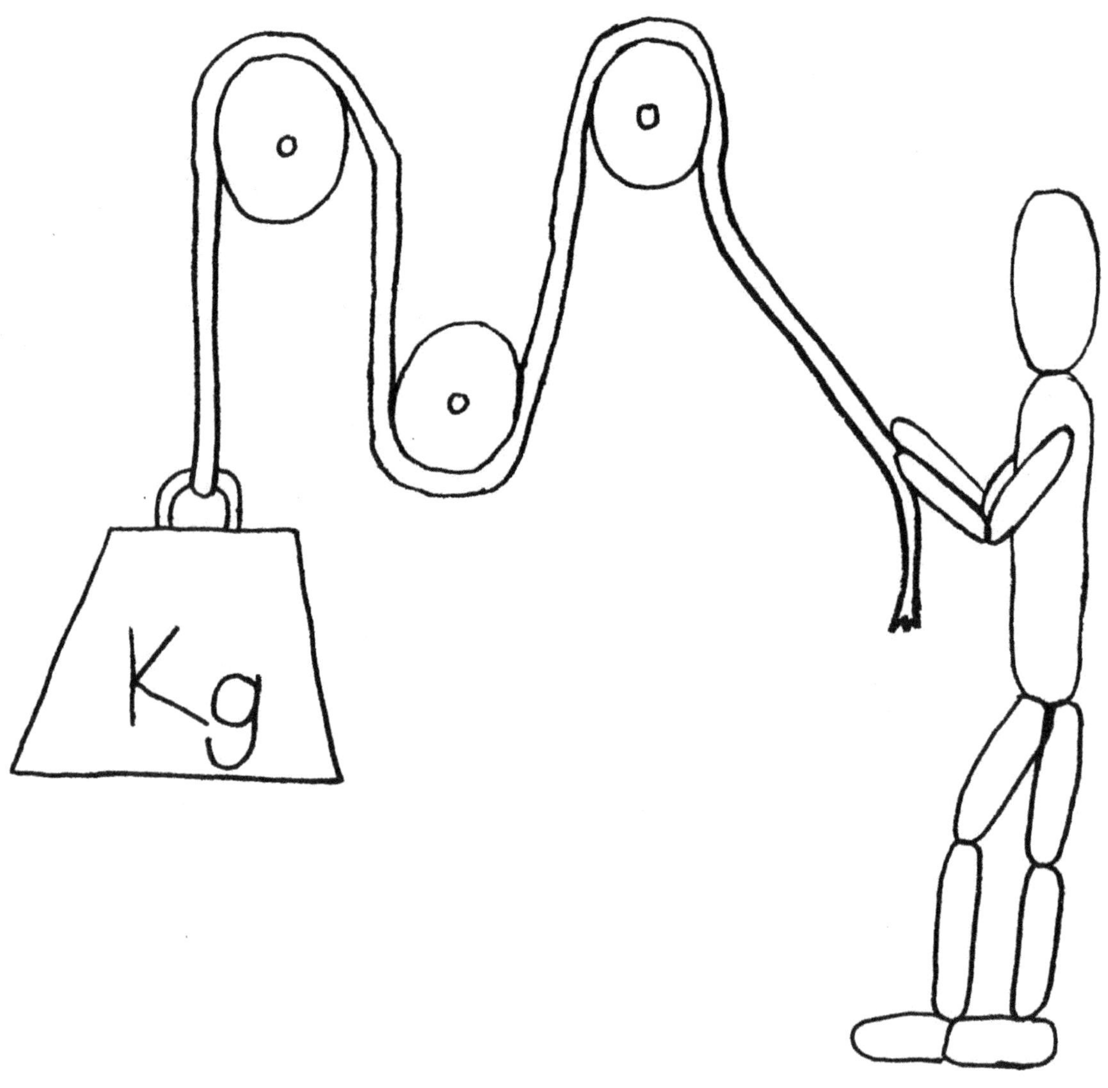

Pulleys can help you lift a heavy load.

Pulley Things Along

What I learned:

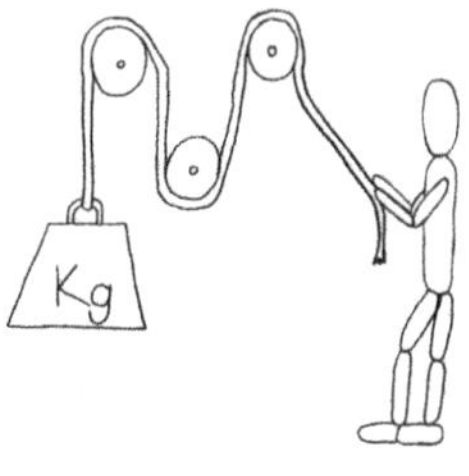

Model Pulley

Ants

Light is the energy that helps us to see.

The Reflection Direction

What I learned:

Reflection Collage

The Sun

Intro to Science

Unit 3: Geology Diary

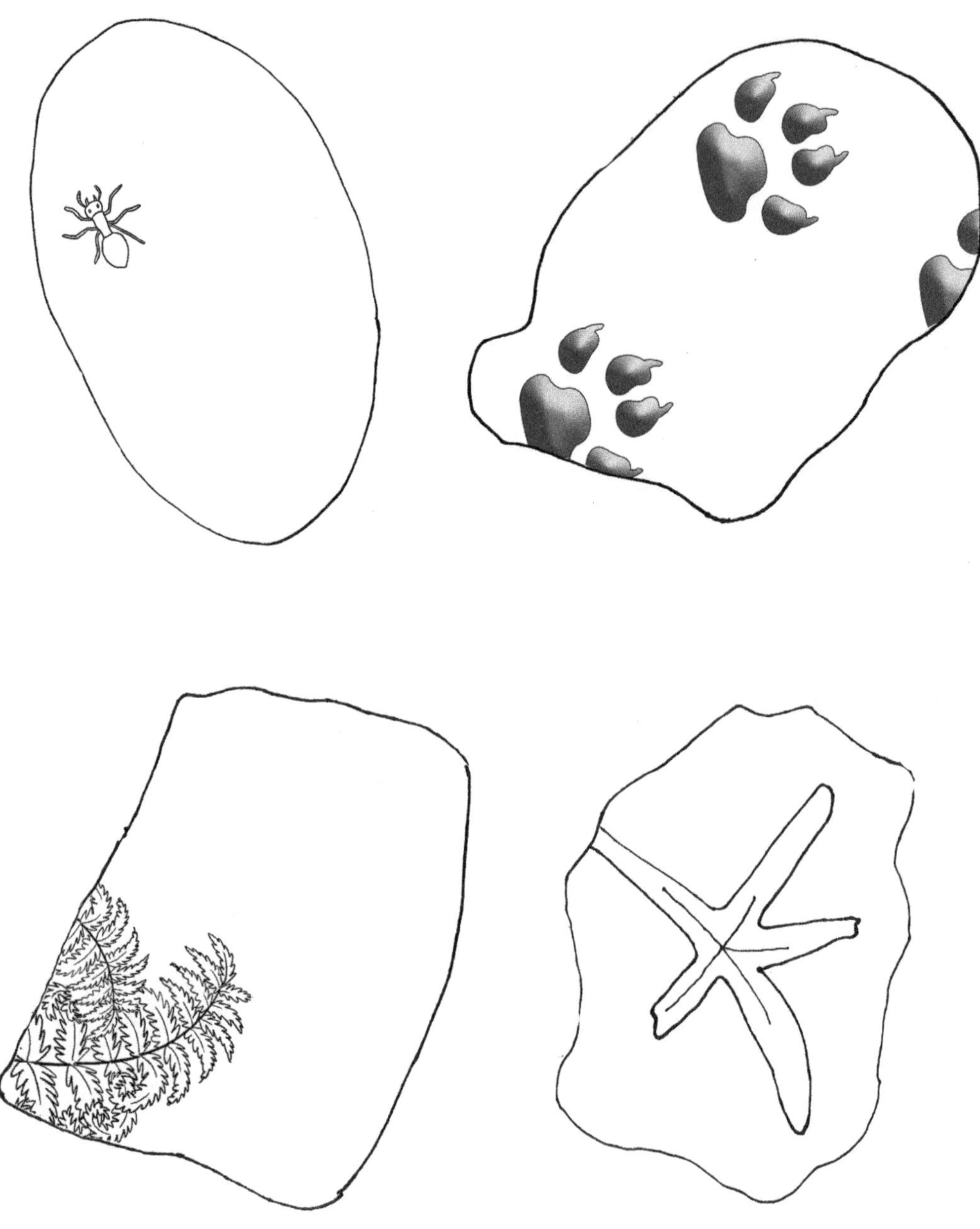

Fossils are imprints of long-gone plants or animals.

Stir-in Fossils

What I learned:

Fossil Prints

Fossil Find

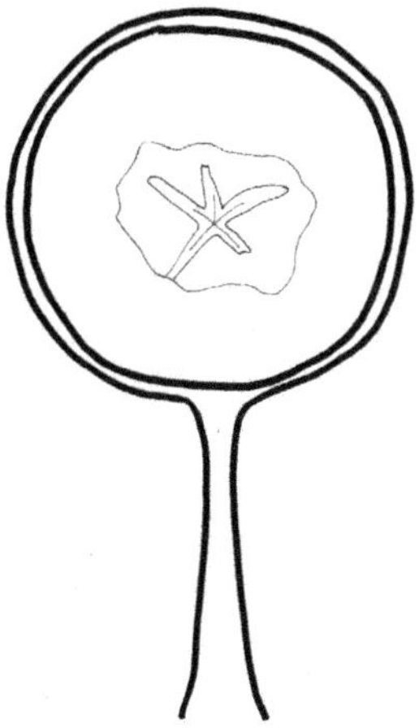

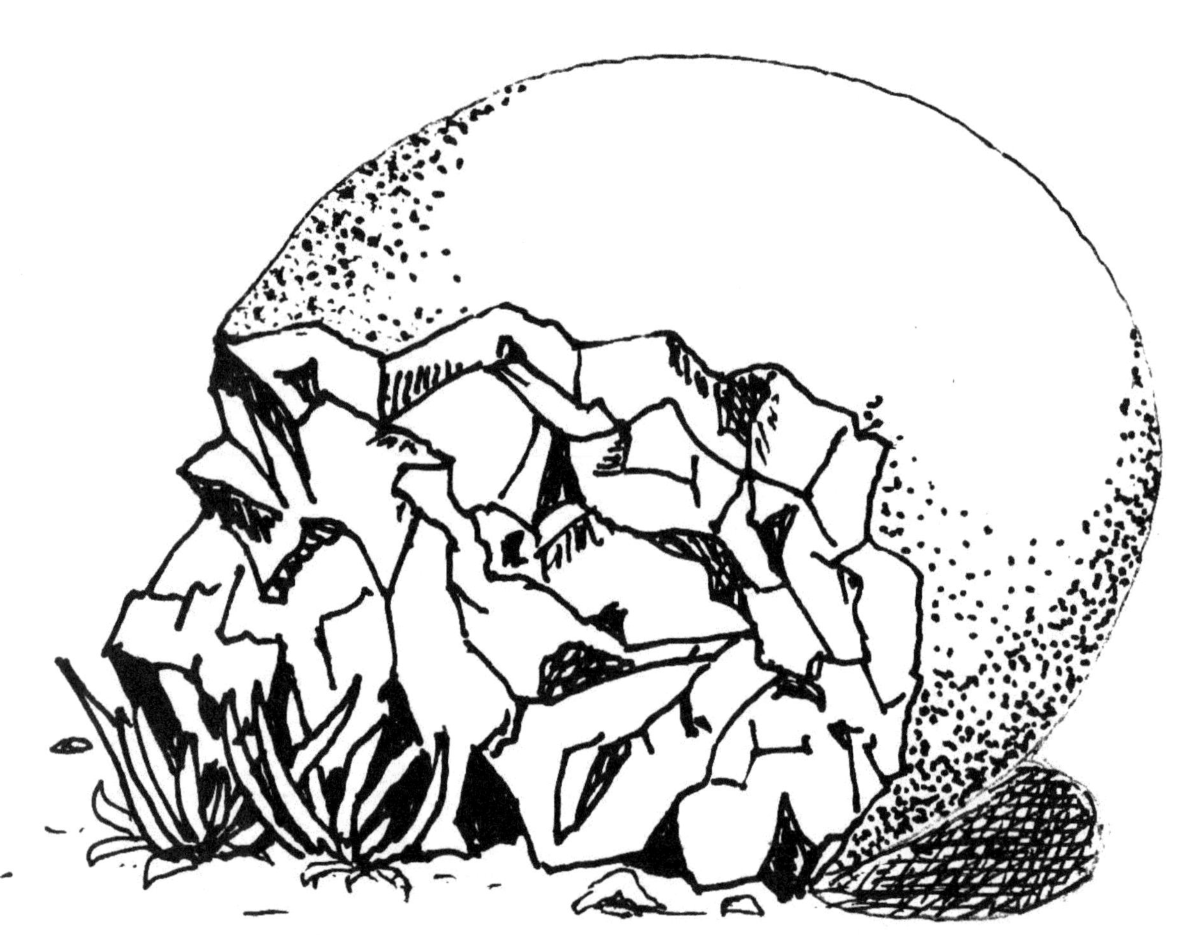

There are many different types of rocks.

Pet Rocks on Parade

What I learned:

Painting Rocks

Rock Hunt

Metamorphic rocks are rocks that have changed.

The Acid Test

Type of rock	Did it bubble or fizz?
	Yes No
	Yes No
	Yes No
	Yes No
	Yes No

What I learned:

____

____

____

____

Metamorphic Art

Metamorphic Rock

Volcanoes explode hot, sticky rock from inside the Earth.

Instant Volcano

What I learned:

My Volcano

Igneous Rock

Sedimentary rock is made from layers of sand, mud, or pebbles.

Cleaning Muddy Water

Before

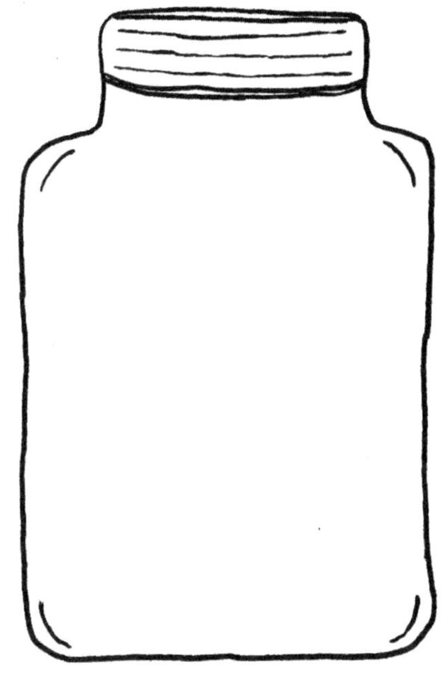

After

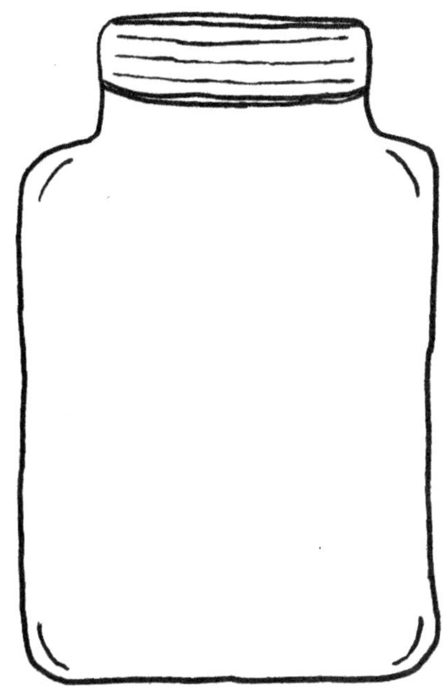

What I learned:

Sand Painting

Sedimentary Rock

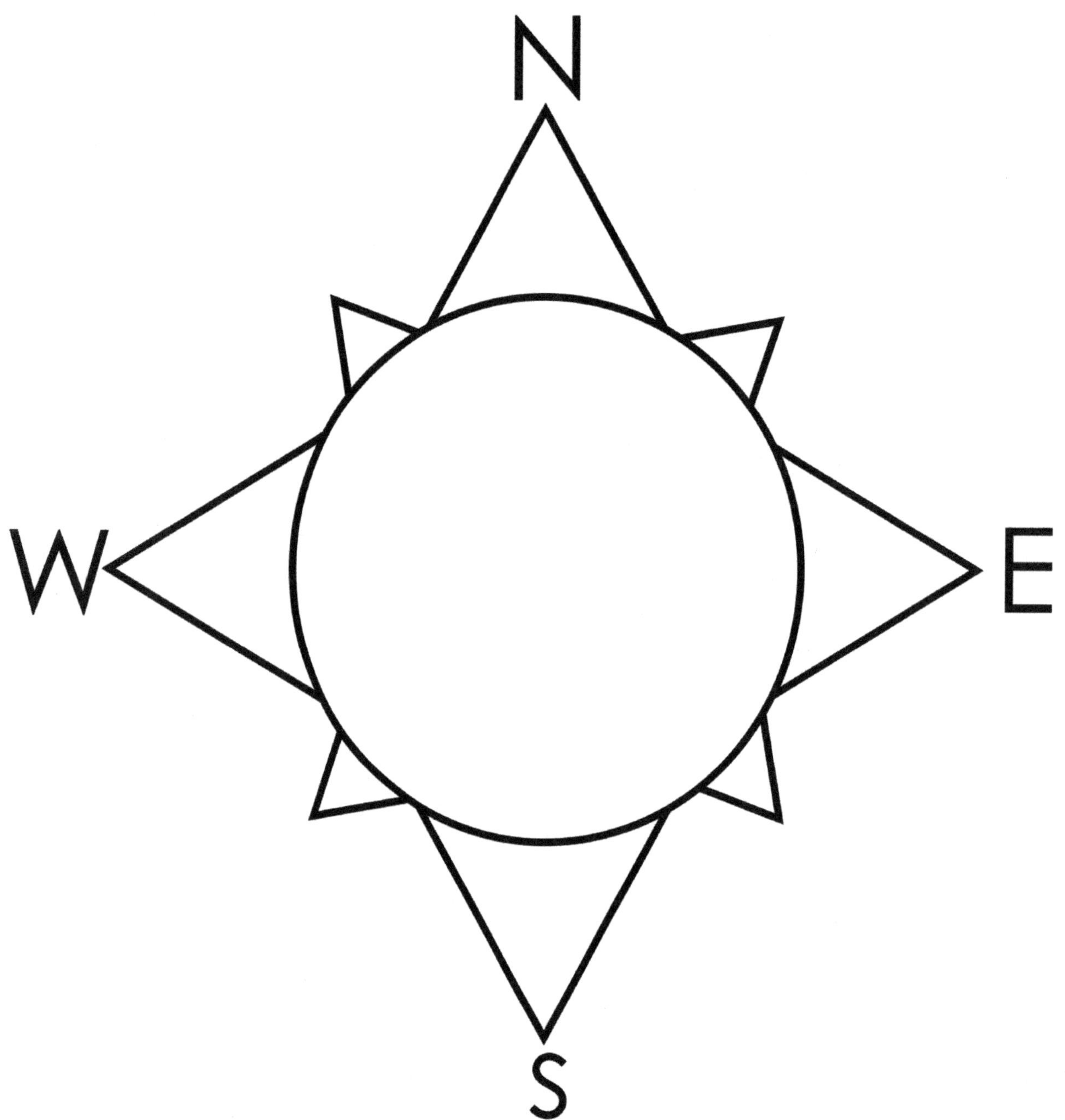

A compass shows us
north, south, east, and west.

Head North, Child, North

What I learned:

N
W E
S

Room Map

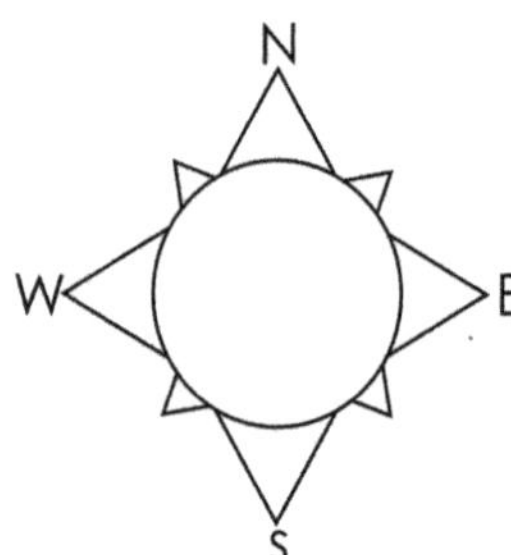

Nature Map

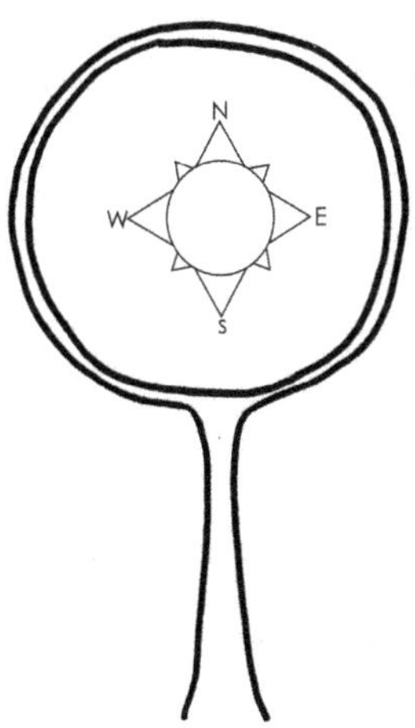

Intro to Science

Unit 4: Meteorology Diary

The energy from the sun heats our earth.

Solar Warmer

What I learned:

Tissue Paper Sun

Sunny Observations

The water cycle shows the movement of water on the earth.

Let's Dew It

What I learned:

Raindrop Painting

Dewy Observations

Spring, summer, fall,
and winter are all seasons.

The Big Meltdown

Which cup melted more ice?	
Red cup with salt	Blue cup without salt

What I learned:

Seasons Collage

Seasonal Tree Study

When air moves it causes wind.

Blow Wind Blow

What I learned:

Draw a Storm

Wind

Tornadoes are funnels of spinning wind.

Tornado Tower

What I learned:

Swirling Art

Tornadoes

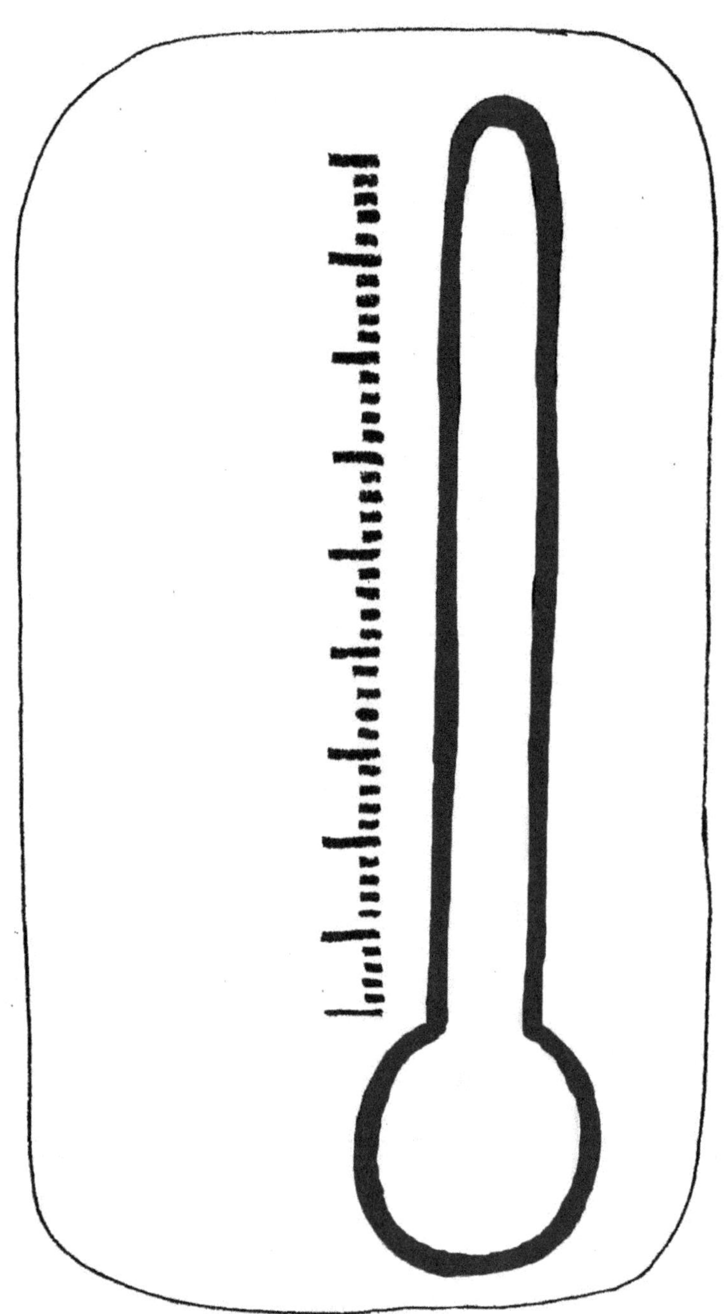

A thermometer tells us whether it is hot or cold.

Hot or Cold: Let's Get Precise

Place	Temperature

Temperature Collage

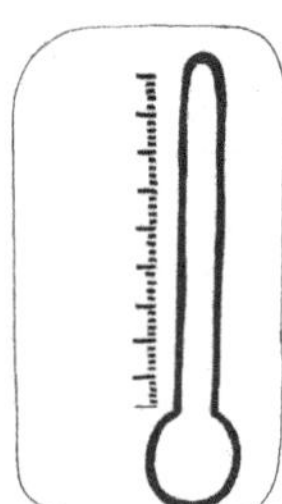

Temperature and Thermometers

Intro to Science

Unit 5: Botany Diary

Plants grow toward the light.

The Amazing Plant Maze

Week 1	Week 2
Week 3	Week 4

Mosaic Plant

Plants

Flowers have the parts of
a plant needed to make a seed.

Dissecting a Flower

What I learned:

Field of Flowers

Flowers

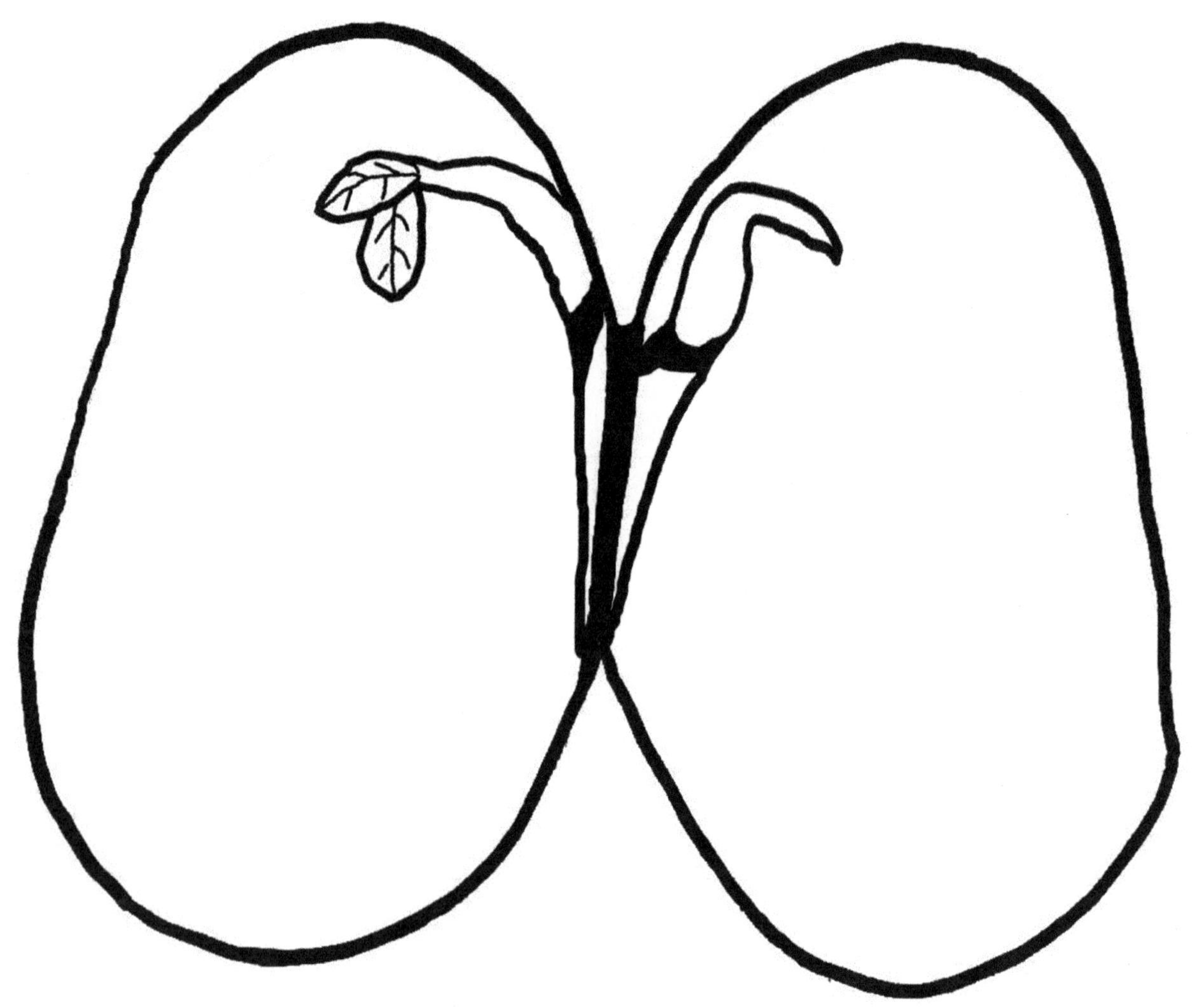

Seeds contain tiny baby plants.

Upside-down Plant

What I learned:

Seed Prints

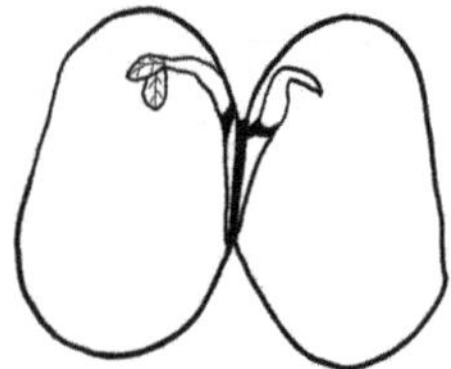

Seeds

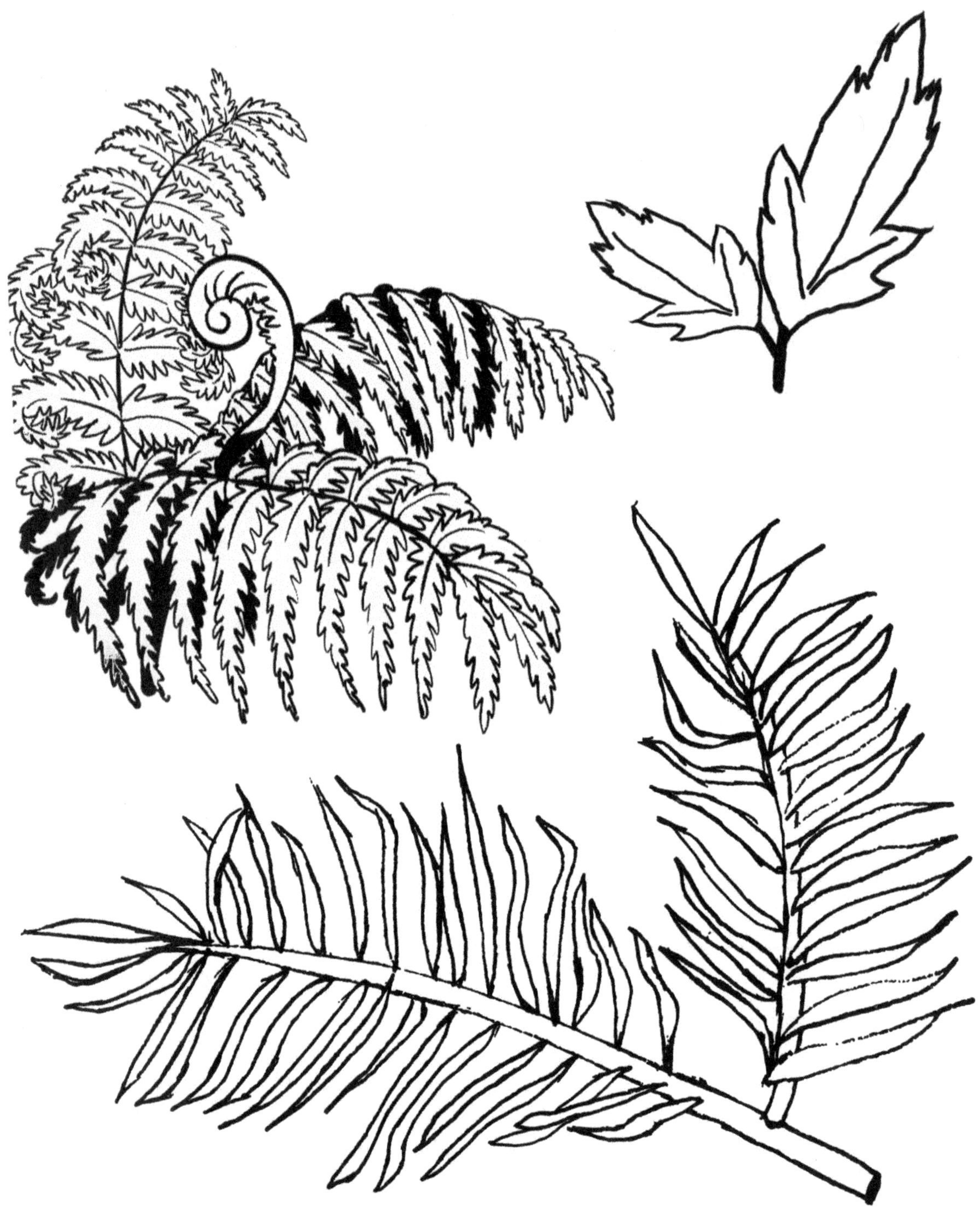

Leaves help the plant to make food.

Leaf Cover-up

In the beginning

After 3 to 4 days

Leaf Rubbings

Leaves

The stem of a plant acts as its highway.

Thirsty Stems

Day 1

Day 3

What I learned:

Blowing Stems

Oak Tree

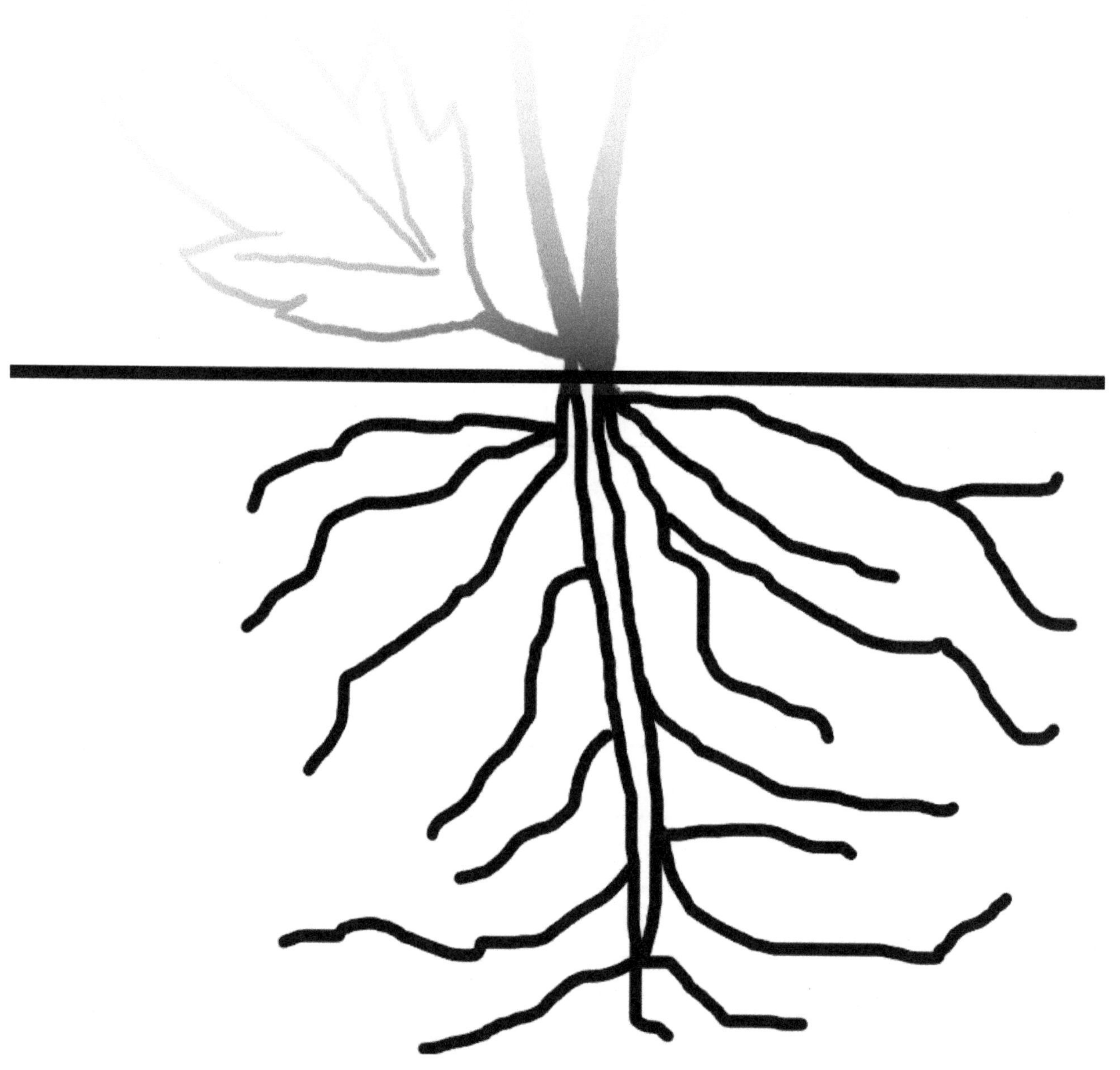

Roots take in water
and nutrients from the soil.

Hydroponics

What I learned:

Painting with Roots

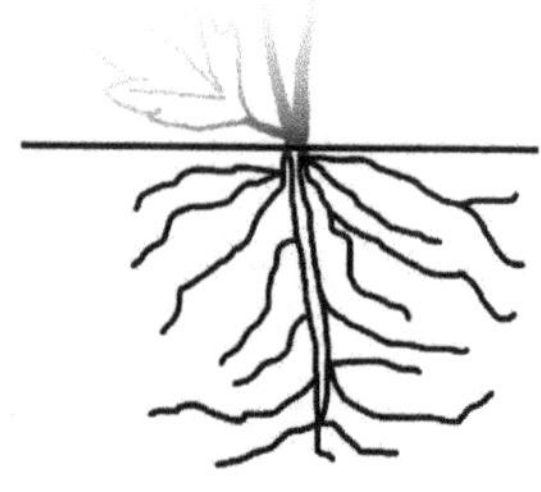

Maple Tree

Intro to Science

Unit 6: Zoology Diary

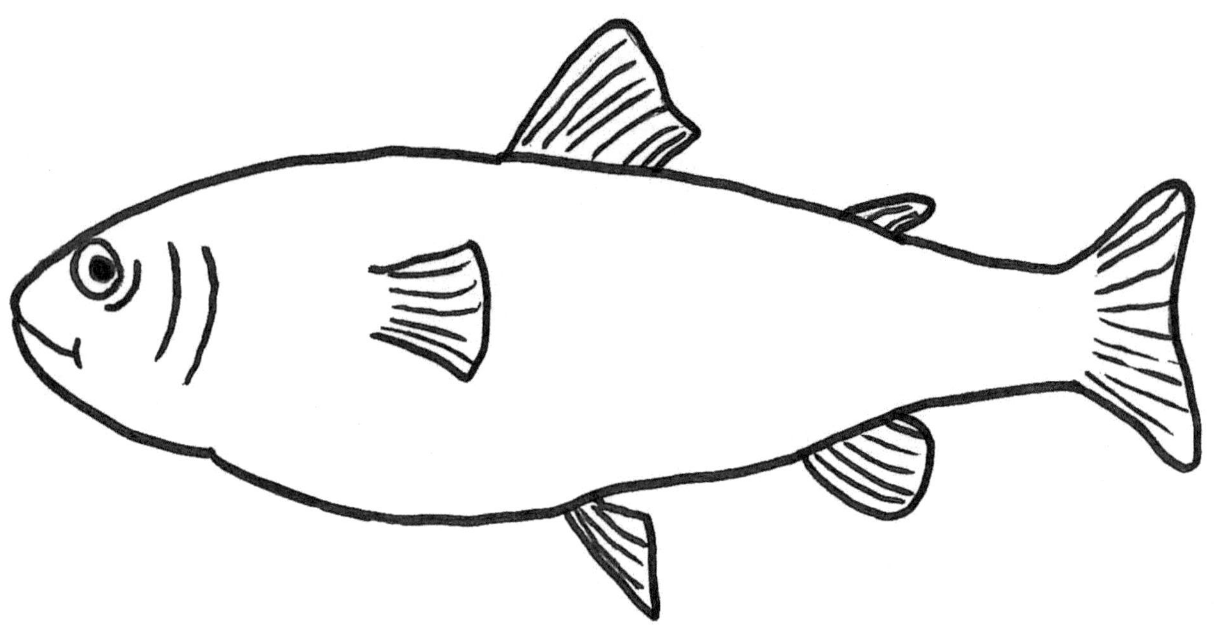

Fish have gills so they can breathe underwater.

Goldfish Tank

What I learned:

Sparkle Fish

Fish

Caterpillars make a chrysalis and then come out as a butterfly.

Cool Off a Fly

What I learned:

Butterfly Beauty

Butterflies

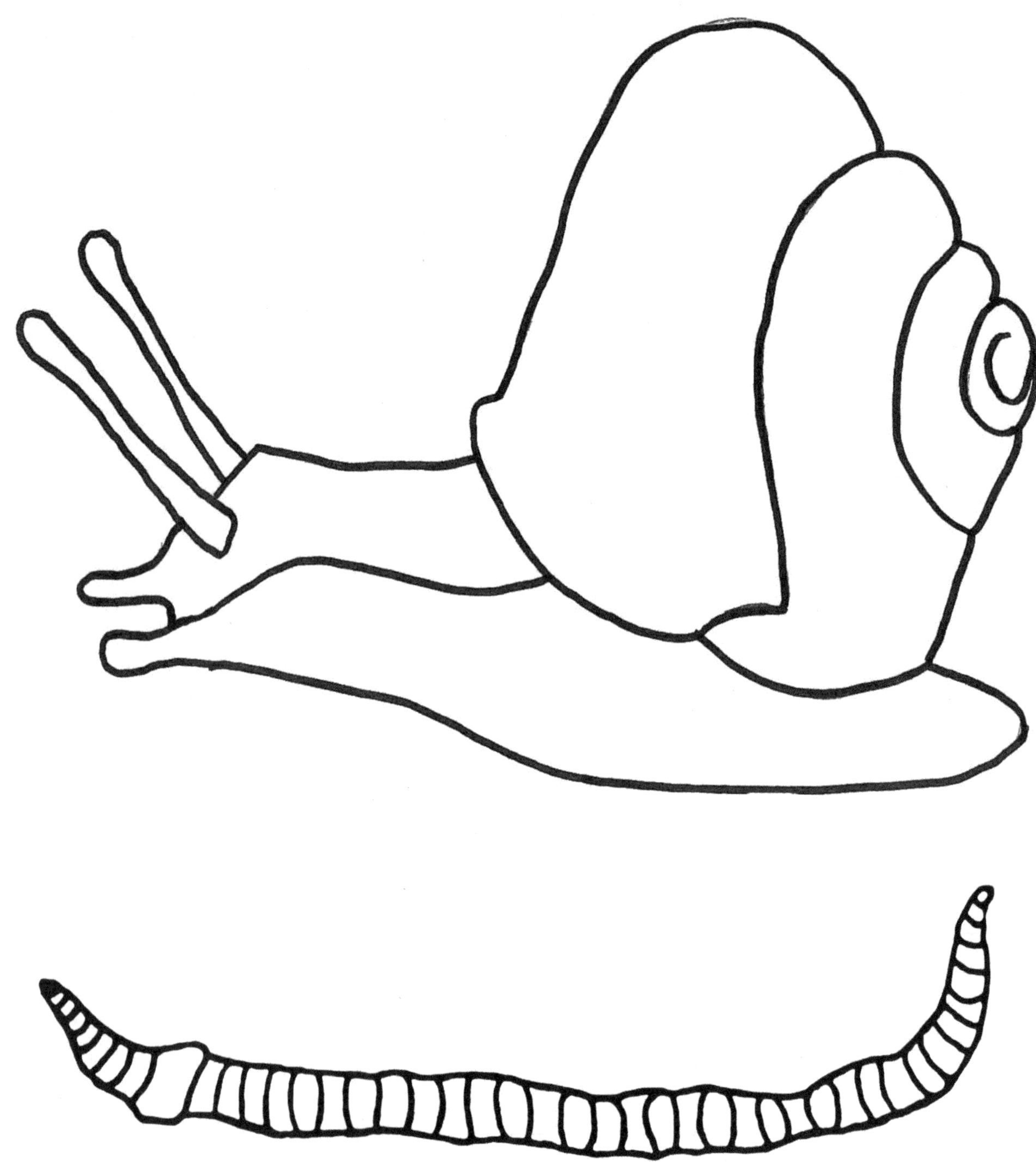

Invertebrates, like snails
and worms, have no backbones.

Earthworm Grand Prix

What I learned:

Worm Trails

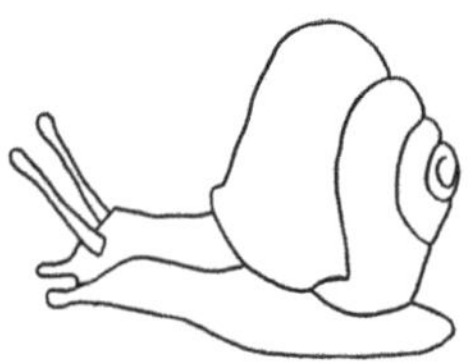

Garden Snails

Mammals, like rabbits, have fur or hair.

Compare Me to Them

Name of the Animal			
Hair			
Teeth			
Hands			
Nose			
Eat			

Mammal Collage

Rabbits

Reptiles, like snakes, are cold-blooded.

Cold-blooded

	Initial Temperature	Temperature after 2 minutes
Thermometer in the Sun		
Thermometer in the Shade		

What I learned:

____

____

____

____

____

____

____

Fingerprint Snakes

Reptiles

Birds have wings and feathers.

No Bones About It

What I learned:

Feather Painting

Birds

Made in USA - North Chelmsford, MA
1065440_9781935614654
03.31.2020 1040